CW00351923

# mother and
# toddler journal

_____

# mother and
# toddler journal

RYLAND
PETERS
& SMALL

LONDON NEW YORK

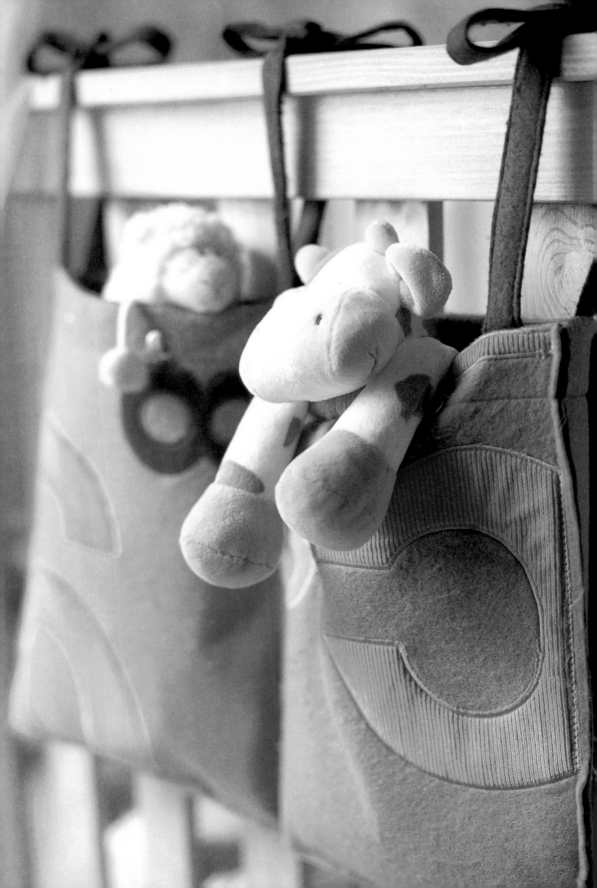

# contents

introduction                6

every day                   9

new experiences            87

celebrations              119

## How to use this journal

These days more and more mothers work or run a busy household, which can leave little time in the day for mother and toddler to spend quality time together. This journal is a fun and easy way for you and your child to sit down and interact in a relaxed and easy environment. It's also a great learning tool, as it promotes verbal and memory skills and provides a loving, bonding experience for both mother and toddler.

This is intended as an occasional journal that invites you to pick the entry that has the most relevance for you and your toddler that day. For example, if your child attends preschool, you might want to choose a page that asks your toddler about his or her activities at school that day. All the entries work in the same way. Each one contains enough space for your child to draw a couple of pictures depicting elements of their day. There's also room for you to write down a brief description of the day in your toddler's own words. Alternatively, you can stick in photos or other artworks, or use the space for more notes.

Each entry ends with a 'sentence starter' for you, the parent, to complete. It may ask what your favorite activity with your toddler is, or what you enjoyed most about the day. After completing the entry, read it to your child so they know just how much you love them, then top it off with a big hug and kiss!

For a toddler, even the most humdrum everyday experiences are fresh, exciting and new. Your child will love sharing his or her thoughts with you and enjoying your undivided attention. Discussing your toddler's day will help develop language skills, while drawing in the journal provides your child with a valuable creative outlet.

month:_____   date:___   year:___

I had so much fun today!

Today I:

_____
_____
_____
_____
_____
_____

# Today mommy told me a story

I love _____ because:

month:_____    date:___    year:___

I love to learn

My favorite learning activity is:

_____
_____
_____
_____
_____
_____

# ABC

## Mommy teaches me so many things!

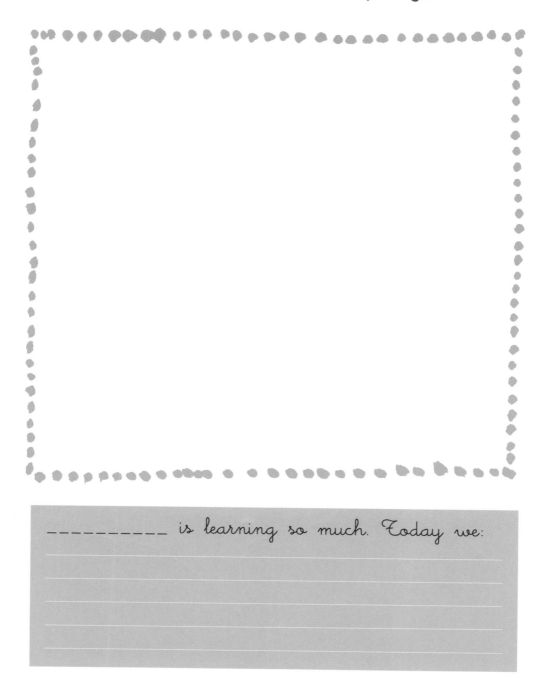

_____ is learning so much. Today we:

month:_____   date:___   year:___

## I like going to preschool

This is what happened today at preschool:

_____
_____
_____
_____
_____
_____

## Here's a picture of me being a good helper:

A book we always enjoy is:

month:_____   date:___   year:___

# Today I played make-believe

This is the game I made up:

## Mommy and I love playing together!

I love to play with _ _ _ _ _ _ _ _ _ because:

_____
_____
_____
_____

month: _ _ _ _ _ _ _    date: _ _ _    year: _ _ _

I had a playdate today

My playdate was fun because:

_____

_____

_____

_____

_____

_____

Today Mommy and I made _____ together.

a song I like to sing to _____ is:

month:_____    date:___    year:___

## I went to the supermarket today

## I like going to the supermarket because:

_____
_____
_____
_____
_____
_____

## Here's a picture of me at the supermarket:

_____ is such a good little helper!

## I did some crafting today

## I love crafting because:

_____

_____

_____

_____

_____

_____

# A game I played today was:

I think _____ is so special because:

month:_____    date:_____    year:_____

I love sport!

I like playing sport because:

_____

_____

_____

_____

_____

# Here's a picture of me playing sport:

I have fun playing with _____ because:

_____

_____

_____

_____

_____

month:_ _ _ _ _ _ _     date:_ _ _     year:_ _ _

Today I went to:

And when I got there, I:

_____

_____

_____

_____

_____

_____

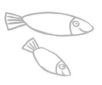

# Here's a picture of what I ate for lunch:

a fun place for us to visit is:

month:_____    date:___    year:___

I love acting silly!

My favorite silly thing to do is:

_____

_____

_____

_____

_____

## Here's a picture of Mommy acting silly!

One particularly cute thing you do or say is:

month:_____ date:____ year:____

I went swimming today

I love swimming because:
_____
_____
_____
_____
_____

# We had so much fun splashing around!

The best part of our day at the pool was:

month:_____    date:___    year:___

I'm a star!

I was a star today because:

_____
_____
_____
_____
_____
_____

# My Mommy is a star too!

_____ has so many star qualities, such as:

month:_____ date:___ year:___

# I went to the park today

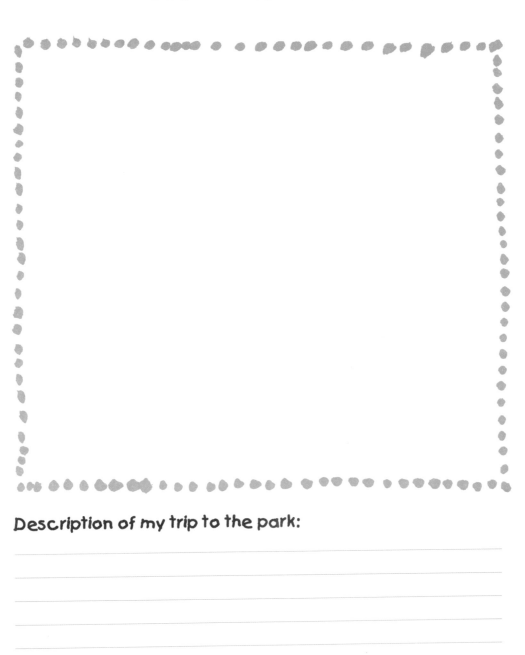

## Description of my trip to the park:

_____

_____

_____

_____

_____

_____

## At the park I saw:

For me, the best part of the day was:

month:_____    date:___    year:___

## My favorite animal

I like this animal because:

## Mommy's favorite animal is:

My favorite animal moment with _____ is:

month:_____    date:___    year:___

Today I went to:

And when I got there, I:

_____

_____

_____

_____

_____

# Here's a picture of what I ate for lunch:

A fun place for us to visit is:

month:_____    date:___    year:___

## Today is a rainy day

## What I did on this rainy day:

_____

_____

_____

_____

_____

_____

## Here's a picture of me splashing in the rain:

*I enjoy rainy days with _____ because:*

month:_____    date:___    year:___

I had so much fun today!

Today I:

_____
_____
_____
_____
_____
_____

# Today mommy told me a story

I love _ _ _ _ _ _ _ _ _ _ because:

month:_____     date:___     year:___

## Best friends

## I like my best friend because:

_____

_____

_____

_____

_____

_____

## Here's a picture of me playing with my best friend:

A song I like to sing to _____ is:

month:_____  date:___  year:___

# I went to the movies today!

## I liked the movie because:

_____
_____
_____
_____
_____
_____

# I love watching a movie with Mommy!

My best cuddles with _____ are:

month:_____ date:___ year:___

## My favorite kind of art is:

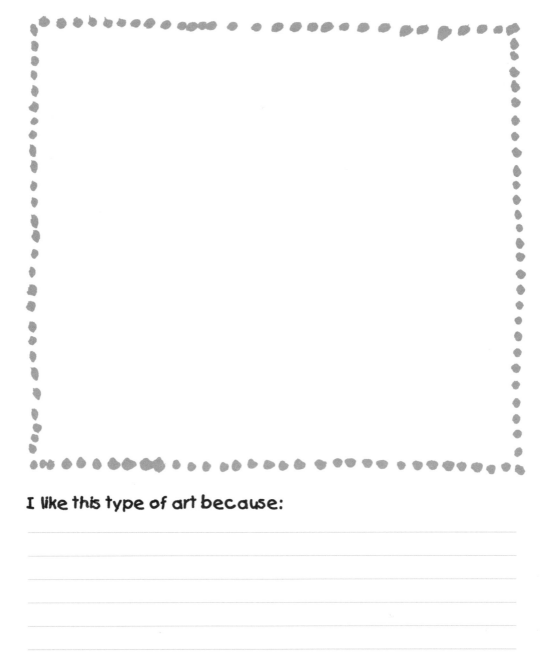

I like this type of art because:

_____

_____

_____

_____

_____

_____

# Here's a picture of me doing my art:

The best part of getting creative with _____ is:

month:_ _ _ _ _ _ _ date:_ _ _ year:_ _ _

## I'm a star!

I was a star today because:

_____

_____

_____

_____

_____

# My Mommy is a star too!

_____ has so many star qualities, such as:

month:_____    date:___    year:___

**Cooking is fun!**

Here's a list of yummy foods that I like to eat:

_____

_____

_____

_____

_____

_____

# Here's a picture of me helping to cook:

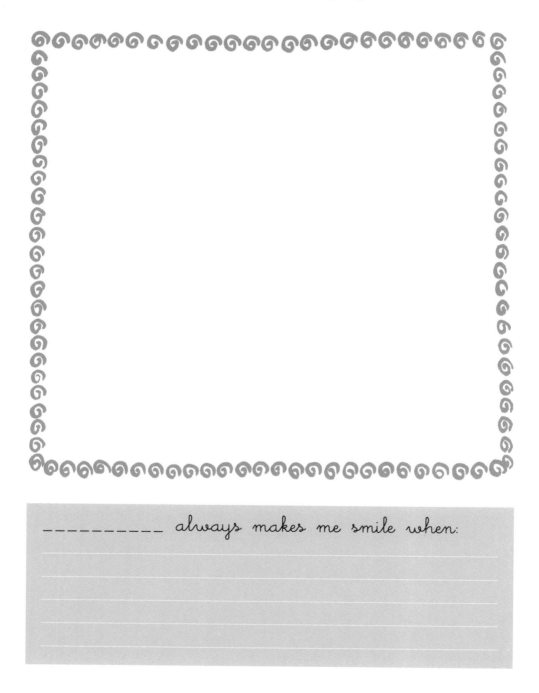

_____ always makes me smile when:

month:_ _ _ _ _ _ _    date:_ _ _    year:_ _ _

## I like going to preschool

This is what happened today at preschool:

_____

_____

_____

_____

_____

_____

## Here's a picture of me being a good helper:

A book we always enjoy is:

# I did some crafting today

## I love crafting because :

_____
_____
_____
_____
_____
_____

# Here's a picture of me playing:

I think _____ is so special because:

month:_____    date:___    year:___

## I went to the park today!

## Description of my trip to the park:

_____

_____

_____

_____

_____

_____

## This is what I saw at the park:

For me, the best part of the day was:

month:_____ date:___ year:___

Today I went to:

And when I got there, I:

_____

_____

_____

_____

_____

_____

# Here's a picture of what I ate for lunch:

A fun place for us to visit is:

month: _ _ _ _ _ _ _   date: _ _ _   year: _ _ _

## Today is a sunny day

**What I did on this sunny day:**

_____

_____

_____

_____

_____

## Here's a picture of me playing in the sunshine:

I enjoy sunny days with _____ because:

month:_____    date:___    year:___

# I had a playdate today

## My playdate was fun because :

_____

_____

_____

_____

_____

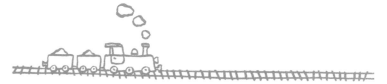

Today Mommy and I made _____together.

A song I like to sing to _____ is:

month:_ _ _ _ _ _ _    date:_ _ _    year:_ _ _

Dancing is so much fun!

My best music to dance to is:

# Here's a picture of me dancing!

I love watching you dance because:

month:_____ date:___ year:___

## I went to the beach today!

## Description of my day at the beach:

_____
_____
_____
_____
_____
_____

I played _____ at the beach

The special part of our trip to the beach was:

month:_____    date:___    year:___

## Today I played make-believe

## This is the game I made up:

_____

_____

_____

_____

_____

_____

## Mommy and I love playing together!

My favorite game with _____ is:

month:_____    date:___    year:___

**I'm a star!**

**I was a star today because:**

# My Mommy is a star too!

_____ has so many star qualities, such as:

month:_____ date:___ year:___

I went swimming today

I love swimming because:

_____

_____

_____

_____

_____

# We had so much fun splashing around!

The best part of our day at the pool was:

month:_ _ _ _ _ _ _    date:_ _ _    year:_ _ _

## I like going to preschool

This is what happened today at preschool:

_____
_____
_____
_____
_____
_____

# Here's a picture of me being a good helper:

A book we always enjoy is:

month:_____   date:___   year:___

I went to the park today

Description of my trip to the park:

_____

_____

_____

_____

_____

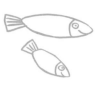

## This is what I saw at the park:

For me, the best part of the day was:

month: _ _ _ _ _ _ _    date: _ _ _    year: _ _ _

I had so much fun today!

Today I:

_____

_____

_____

_____

_____

_____

# Today mommy told me a story

I love _____ because:

month:_____    date:___    year:___

## I did some crafting today

## I love crafting because:

_____

_____

_____

_____

_____

_____

_____

## A game I played today was:

I think _____ is so special because:

# ABC

Toddlers delight in doing new things, mastering new skills, and meeting new people. This chapter covers a range of exciting new experiences for you and your toddler to try out together then discuss and illustrate.

month:_ _ _ _ _ _ _    date:_ _ _    year:_ _ _

# I went to the zoo today!

## Description of my day at the zoo:

_____

_____

_____

_____

_____

_____

# Here's a picture of me at the zoo

The best part of our day at the zoo was:

month:_____    date:___    year:___

## I visited the doctor today

This is what happened when I visited the doctor:

_____
_____
_____
_____
_____

## I like holding Mommy's hand when we go out

_____ was so brave when:

month:_____ date:___ year:___

## I went to a restaurant today

The best thing about the restaurant was:

_____

_____

_____

_____

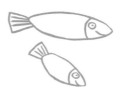

# Here's a picture of the yummy food I ate:

One of _____'s favorite meals is:

month:_____  date:___  year:___

Today I fed the ducks!

I had so much fun when we:

_____
_____
_____
_____
_____

## Mommy and I fed the ducks together:

I thought _____ was so adorable when:

month:_ _ _ _ _ _ _ date:_ _ _ year:_ _ _

# I tried something new today

## It's good to try new things! I tried:

_____

_____

_____

_____

_____

_____

# Today we took a walk, and on our walk we saw:

I love walking with _____ because:

month:_ _ _ _ _ _ _    date:_ _ _    year:_ _ _

# It's snowing today!

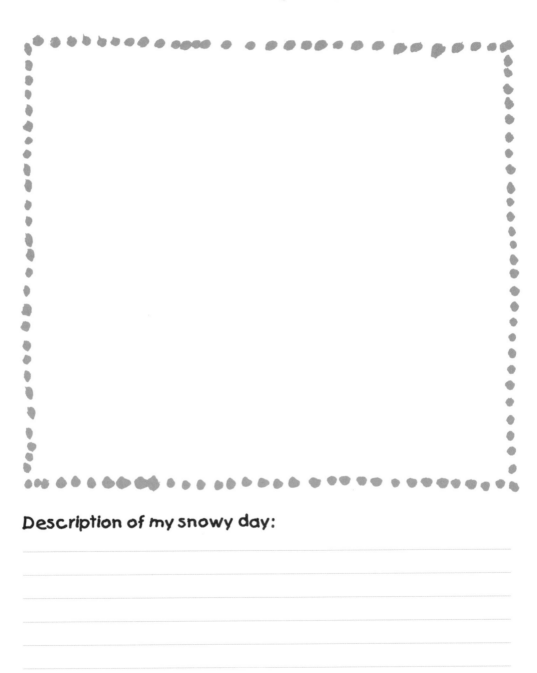

## Description of my snowy day:

_____

_____

_____

_____

_____

_____

# Here's a picture of me playing in the snow:

The best part of our day in the snow was:

month:_____     date:___     year:___

I took a trip to the pet store today!

The animal I liked best at the pet store was:

_____

_____

_____

_____

_____

_____

# These are some of the cute animals at the pet store:

_____ always makes me smile when:

month:_____    date:___    year:___

## I went shopping today

How I helped with the shopping:

_____

_____

_____

_____

_____

_____

## Here's a picture of the things we bought:

_____ did a good job shopping today!

month:_____    date:___    year:___

I visited the doctor today

This is what happened when I visited the doctor:

# I like holding Mommy's hand when we go out

_____ was so brave when:

month: _ _ _ _ _ _ _ _ date: _ _ _ year: _ _ _

Today I got a haircut

This is what happened at the hairdressing salon:

_____
_____
_____
_____
_____
_____

# Here's a picture of me with my new haircut:

_____ did very well at the hairdresser!

month:_____   date:___   year:___

## I tried something new today!

## It's good to try new things! I tried:

_____
_____
_____
_____
_____
_____

## Today we took a walk, and on our walk we saw:

I love walking with _____ because:

month:_____    date:___    year:___

Today mommy took me to get new shoes

The best thing about the shoe store was:

_____

_____

_____

_____

_____

_____

_____

## Here's a picture of my new shoes:

_____ did such a great job of getting new shoes fitted today!

month:_____  date:___  year:___

## I tried some yummy new food today!

## My favorite foods are:

_____

_____

_____

_____

_____

# I love helping to cook

The best part of today was:
_____
_____
_____
_____
_____

month:_____  date:___  year:___

# I visited a museum today!

Description of my museum visit:

_____
_____
_____
_____
_____
_____

## Here's a picture of my favorite exhibit

I thought the best part of our day was:

Special occasions such as birthdays, anniversaries, and other celebrations are at the very heart of family life. Toddlers grow up in the blinking of an eye, so make sure you record these happy memories. You and your child will treasure them in years to come.

month:_____  date:___  year:___

Happy New Year!

Today was lots of fun because:

_____
_____
_____
_____
_____
_____

# Here's a picture of my favorite New Year moment:

This year, _ _ _ _ _ _ _ _ _ _ and I will:

month:_____    date:___    year:___

Happy Valentine's Day

Valentine's Day is special because:

# I love my Mommy so much because:

To celebrate Valentine's Day, we:

month:_____   date:___   year:___

## Happy Mother's Day!

Mother's Day is special because:

## For Mother's Day I gave Mommy a:

Mother's Day was magical this year because:

_____
_____
_____
_____
_____

month:_____    date:___    year:___

## We're going on vacation

On vacation it was a lot of fun because:

_____
_____
_____
_____
_____
_____
_____

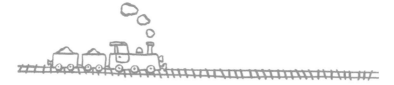

# The best part of my vacation was:

A special memory of our trip is:

month:_____  date:___  year:___

Hurray! It's my birthday today!

This is how we celebrated my birthday:

_____

_____

_____

_____

_____

_____

# Here's a picture of some of my gifts:

When I think of _____'s birth, I remember:

month:_____   date:___   year:___

## Happy Halloween

## This is what I did on Halloween:

_____
_____
_____
_____
_____
_____

## Here's a picture of me dressed up on Halloween:

The best part of Halloween with _____ is:

month:_____    date:___    year:___

Today I went on a visit

We went to visit:

_____
_____
_____
_____
_____
_____

# I love visiting people and making new friends!

The best time of day with _____ is:

_____

_____

_____

_____

month:_____ date:\_\_\_ year:\_\_\_

## Happy Thanksgiving!

## We celebrate Thanksgiving because:

# I helped at Thanksgiving by:

The best part of Thanksgiving was:

month:_____  date:___  year:___

## We had a special family celebration today

The reason for the celebration was:

_____

_____

_____

_____

_____

_____

# Today I helped celebrate by:

The best part of being part of a family is:

month:_____ date:____ year:____

Today it was _____'s birthday!

My special birthday gift to _____ was:

_____

_____

_____

_____

_____

_____

On _____'s birthday I wore:

I love seeing _____'s face light up when:

month:_____    date:___    year:___

☆ ☆

## Soon it will be Christmas!

## Christmas is a special time when:

_____

_____

_____

_____

_____

_____

# Here's a picture of me at Christmas:

My most magical Christmas memory is:

# picture credits

**All illustrations by Robert Merrett**

*Photography credits*

Vanessa Davies: page 2

Winfried Heinze: page 4

Sandra Lane: page 119

Daniel Pangbourne: back jacket; pages 9, 86, 87

Debi Treloar: page 8

Polly Wreford: front jacket; page 118

**Text by Jennifer Lugo-Stockham**

**Designer** Luis Peral Aranda
**Commissioning editor** Annabel Morgan
**Picture research** Emily Westlake
**Production** Toby Marshall
**Art director** Leslie Harrington
**Publishing director** Alison Starling

First published in the UK in 2009 by
Ryland Peters & Small
20–21 Jockey's Fields
London WC1R 4BW

and in the USA by
Ryland Peters & Small, Inc.,
519 Broadway, 5th Floor
New York, NY 10012

www.rylandpeters.com

Text © Jennifer Lugo-Stockham 2009
Design, illustrations, and photography
© Ryland Peters & Small 2009

10 9 8 7 6 5 4 3 2 1

All rights reserved. No part of this
publication may be reproduced,
stored in a retrieval system, or
transmitted in any form or by any
means, electronic, mechanical,
photocopying or otherwise, without
the prior permission of the publisher.

ISBN 978-1-84597-903-4

Printed and bound in China